christmas?

MR. GONOPOLIS AND HIS 12 HOLSTEINS

20th ANNIVERSARY EDITION

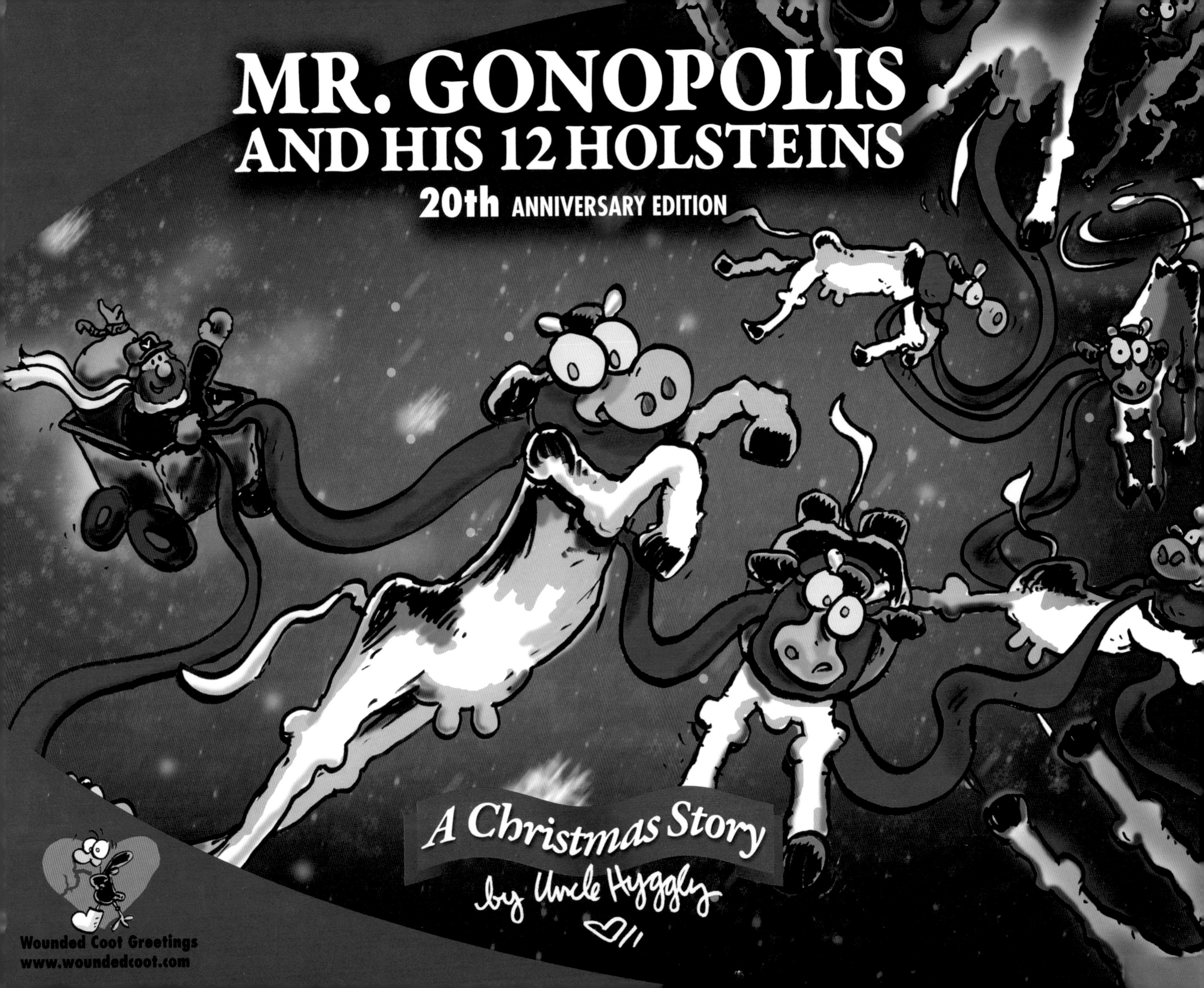

A Christmas Story

by Uncle Hyggly

Wounded Coot Greetings
www.woundedcoot.com

For Elise, who adds the color to my world
(and taught me to eat my vegetables).

Wounded Coot Greetings
www.woundedcoot.com
19350 Ireland Court, Lakeville, MN 55044
© 2005 by Uncle Hyggly, aka Charles Smith-Dewey

Manufactured in China.

No coots were destroyed to manufacture this book; however, four may have been accidentally maimed.

The names shown on Santa's "nice" list are for illustrative purposes only, and are no guarantee of presents on Christmas morning. Past performance may not be an accurate indicator of future results (stay good!).

No actual cows were traced to provide the amazing lifelike images in this book. We tried, but they wouldn't hold still.

ISBN-13: 978- 0-935583-10-6
ISBN-10:   0-935583-10-6

'was the 24th of the month that did follow November

When the call did go out to one special member

Of the Emergency, Substitute Santa Claus Corps

And no one remembered it happening before!

Ole Gonopolis picked up his phone
And he heard Santa let out a
sorrowful moan

And he heard Santa tell him,
through sniffles and sneezles
That Doc Elf had told him:
"It's possibly measles"

"I do not feel good
and I can't drive my sleigh

That means no gifts for
the kids Christmas Day

The thought of those children,
all crying and sobbing

Fills Santa's head
with a horrible throbbing "

"*But how can that be?*" you ask, raising your eyebrow
"*How can it be that 12 holsteins can fly now?*"
The adrenaline flowed, as they shook with a titter,
And each bovine hair on each bovine did flitter ...

"On Jessie, on Sally, on Gertrude and Mary,
On Karma, on Clara, on Hulda and Carrie,

On Oprah, on Sigrid," he yelled with some gust,
This old storage box is beginning to rust!"

They departed the farm,
their tails swayin' and switchin',

While Mrs. Gonopolis
waved goodbye the kitchen.

All through the night
they stuck fast to their route

Flying south to St. Paul
and then "nort to D'Lute"

The wind, *it blew hard,*
as it waffled and wangled,

'Til 12 holstein cows
in 12 scarves became

TANGLED!

They twisted and turned,
and the wagon went spinning

They were locked in a battle
— and the weather was winning!

They dropped through the skies
like a bucket of lead

They crashed to a rooftop
and crumpled like bread!

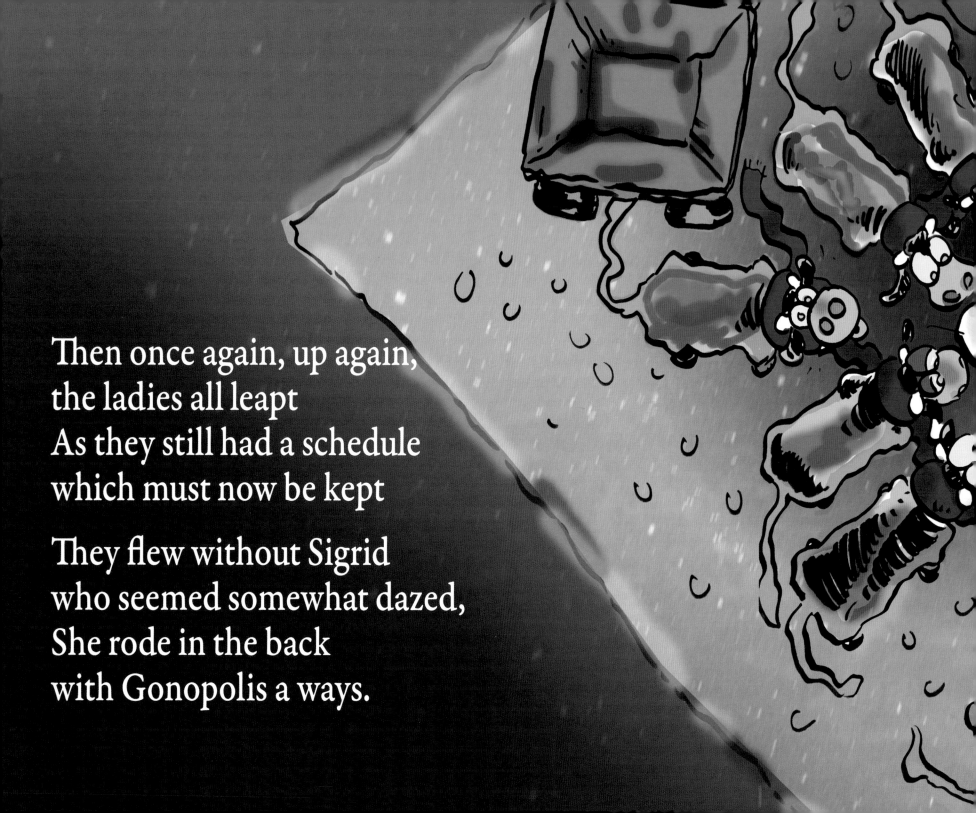

Then once again, up again,
the ladies all leapt
As they still had a schedule
which must now be kept

They flew without Sigrid
who seemed somewhat dazed,
She rode in the back
with Gonopolis a ways.

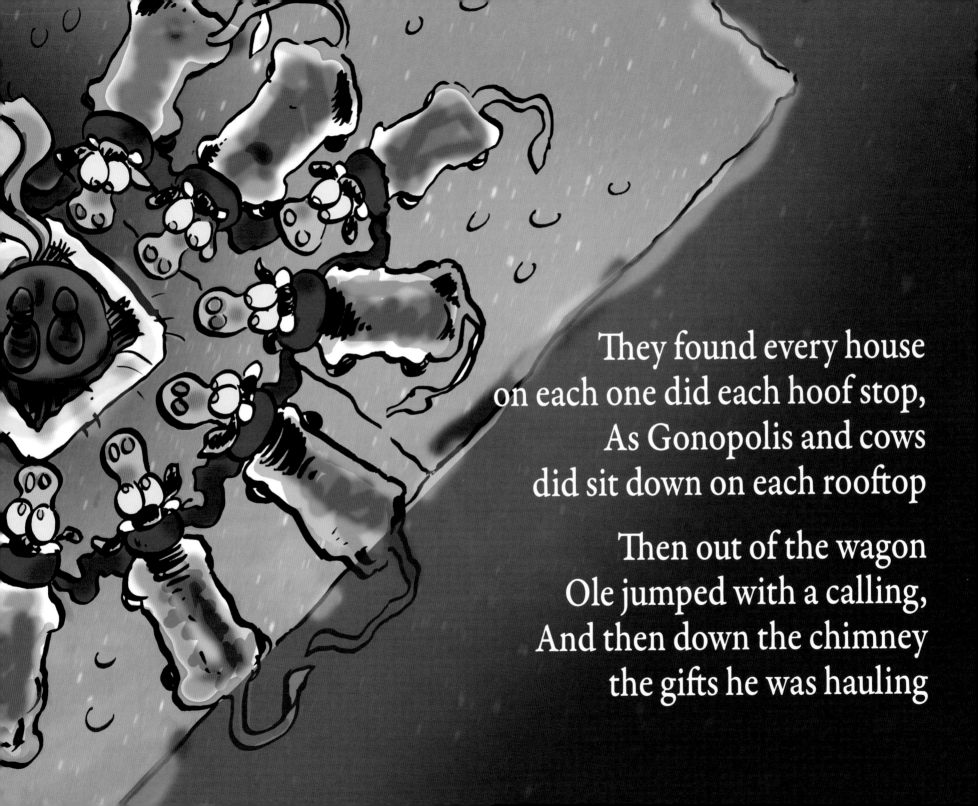

They found every house
on each one did each hoof stop,
As Gonopolis and cows
did sit down on each rooftop

Then out of the wagon
Ole jumped with a calling,
And then down the chimney
the gifts he was hauling

He tiptoed past rooms where the children did slumber,
Each foot sliding gently on *old* creaky lumber ...

He yapped and he howled and he bayed and he barked,
While Gonopolis floundered about in the dark!

Caught
in the moonlight,
those fish teeth
were glistening

But up on the
rooftop
those holsteins
were listening

They slipped off their scarves,
and lashed them together

It dropped down the chimney
as light as a feather

Gonopolis saw it,
he lunged with a shout,

He grabbed hold that scarf ...

Then out over the ocean,
they went with great speed,
With the holstein named Clara
assuming the lead

Well their journey was long
and the weather was bleary,

And one by one each
holstein cow became weary

Gonopolis yelled "Now you must stay awake,"
But each joint and each bone in each holstein did ache

Their eyelids grew heavy, their muscles were sagging,
And nearer the water their udders were dragging

Then at the moment of sheer desperation,
Gonopolis was blessed with a near inspiration:

"*Hey all youse flies on my cows
quit your napping ...*

*... Open your wings,
shake them out
get them flapping!*"

From all over the cows
from their tails to their heads,

A gaggle of flies
waggled out
from their beds!

The force of their wings hummed in one massive choir
As they lifted up each of those cows slightly higher ...

But those cows were so heavy. and those flies were so slight,
Soon the flies would be finished and then so would the flight!

Gonopolis was tired, his vision was dimming,
And soon Jessie's tail in the water was skimming,

As first one hoof, then two hooves
then three hooves were trailing,

As first two, and then four,
and then six flies were failing

The cows sunk to their ankles,
they sunk to their thighs,

As their auxiliary engines
were dropping like...

... flies

And then all except one of those flies sputtered out.
And all you could see left was poor Bessie's snout.

And suddenly, *that* was no longer about.

But in a few seconds (that seemed like three days)
Out of the ocean those holsteins were raised!
Gonopolis and company to Europe did sail ...

Then once again, up again,
all rested and willing

They flew to the stockings
that needed some filling.

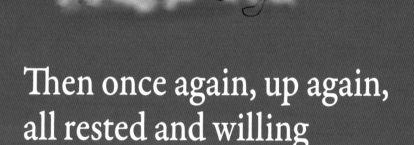

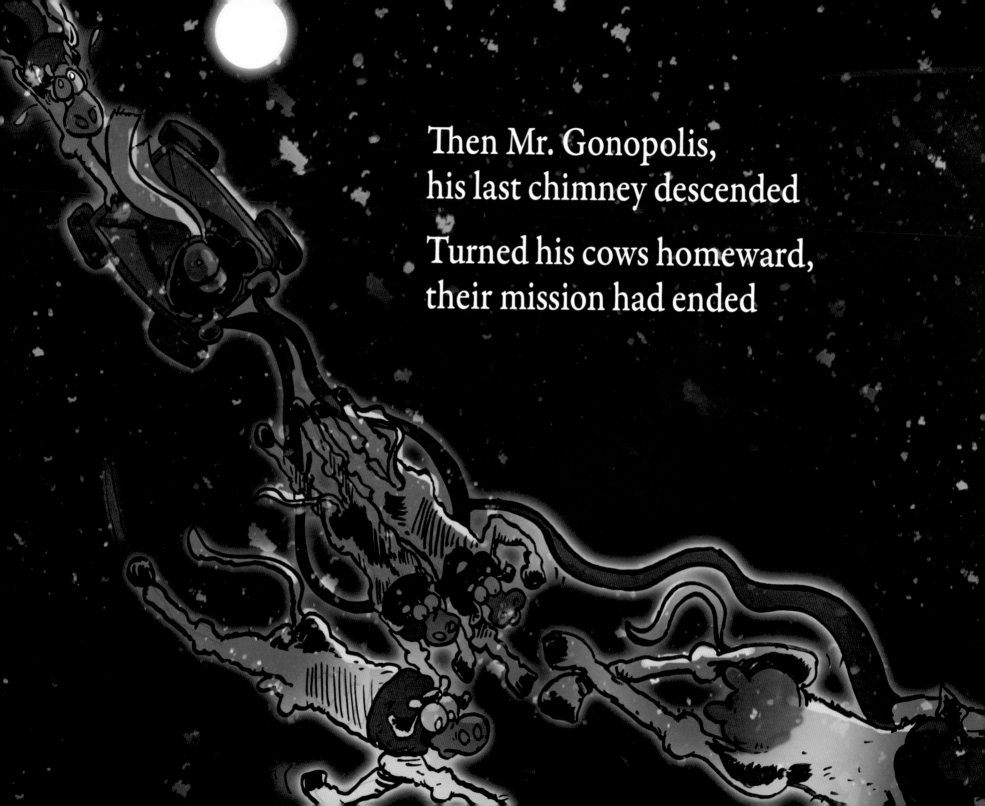

Then Mr. Gonopolis,
his last chimney descended

Turned his cows homeward,
their mission had ended

They arrived at the farm,
with the snow gently blowing

And they drifted to sleep
as the rooster was crowing

Ole's slumber was stolen
by a ring from the wall,

And he roused from his sleep
as he took Santa's call

The truth hit Gonopolis
like a shovel in the head!

His knees turned to jello,
and his face turned beet red!

The gifts he had given
were just some things he'd ...
... found in his shed!

Perhaps no one was quite
as surprised as young Harley,

Who found that his stocking
was plumb full of ... barley!

Or maybe young Frieda
who had wanted a Care Bear.

Who spent
Christmas morning
unwrapping a ...
plow share!

Gonopolis was glum,
he had failed,
he was saddened

'Til Santa let loose
with a laugh
HE was

GLADDENED!

"Gonopolis, my friend, you're a success don'cha know,
It's not the gifts that you give it's the love that you show!

Each child knows you love them, each child knows you care,
There is no greater gift you could possibly share!"

got christmas?